LOOKING AT CHROMOSOMES

by

JOHN McLEISH, Ph.D.

Principal Scientific Officer, Department of Cell Biology

and

BRIAN SNOAD, M.I.Biol.

Senior Experimental Officer, Department of Applied Genetics

John Innes Institute, Bayfordbury, Hertford

MACMILLAN

London · Melbourne · Toronto

ST MARTIN'S PRESS

New York

First Edition 1958
Reprinted 1959, 1962
Reprinted with corrections 1966

MACMILLAN AND COMPANY LIMITED
Little Essex Street London WC 2
also Bombay Calcutta Madras Melbourne

THE MACMILLAN COMPANY OF CANADA LIMITED
70 Bond Street Toronto 2

ST MARTIN'S PRESS INC
175 Fifth Avenue New York NY 10010

PRINTED IN GREAT BRITAIN

PREFACE

PLANTS and animals are made up of cells which contain the substances concerned in heredity. We can begin to understand the mechanism whereby these substances are transmitted from one generation to another from a detailed study of cells under an ordinary high-power microscope. Our aim in this book has been to demonstrate by means of a continuous series of photographs and illustrations, how cells and the hereditary substances they contain behave during the growth of a living organism, how the cells which function in reproduction come to be formed and, finally, how the hereditary substances are passed on from parents to offspring.

There are few living organisms in which all the various phases of cell division are suitably clear for the purposes of demonstration. It has, therefore, been usual to combine observations from a range of plants and animals, each one favourable for the demonstration of particular stages. In our opinion, however, cell behaviour is more easily understood if the observations are confined to one species so that a less interrupted sequence can be obtained. There are some species of flowering plants which are suitable in this respect and it is from one of them, *Lilium regale*, that we have been able to obtain our series of photographs. We are, therefore, primarily concerned with demonstrating the behaviour of the chromosomes in plant cells although we must emphasise that the underlying mechanism of heredity is fundamentally similar in plants and animals.

The book is not intended to be a comprehensive survey of cell behaviour but we hope that the combination of photographs, drawings and text will prove of value to those students with some knowledge of biology who wish to know something of chromosomes. Those who have already started a course of practical cytology may find the photographs of some use in the interpretation of their own preparations.

We have found the Feulgen squash method the most suitable staining technique for demonstrating the chromosomes. Techniques for demonstrating other cell components such as nucleoli, spindles and cytoplasmic bodies are available but if they had been used many of the details of chromosome behaviour would have been obscured.

As no elaborate equipment is needed preparations such as ours can easily be made and we urge those who are interested to make some for themselves. A description of cytological and photographic technique is not within the scope of this book but details can be found in one of the books which we recommend (see Appendix).

We should like to thank Mr. L. S. Clarke, Photographer at this Institute, not only for his helpful advice during the taking of the photographs, but also for his careful preparation of the prints.

J. McL.

B. S.

BAYFORDBURY

January, 1957.

CONTENTS

1

INTRODUCTION

SOME of our earliest historical records contain references to theories concerned with heredity, reproduction and growth. These theories were generally of a wildly speculative nature, frequently based upon superstition and traditional beliefs. This was mainly due to the lack of knowledge of the detailed structure of plants and animals. However, the end of the sixteenth century saw the successful construction of the first compound microscope and this new instrument was destined to revolutionise the study of life. Gradually, as improved models with higher magnifications became available, it was possible to examine the component parts of living organisms in far more detail. Step by step new discoveries were made and these slowly dispelled many of the superstitious ideas which had arisen in the past.

By the end of the seventeenth century it was realised that both plants and animals varied in appearance because the living material of which they were composed could be organised in a variety of ways. It was established by Robert Hooke, Nehemiah Grew and Marcello Malpighi, among others, that this living material was not a single homogeneous mass but was split up into numerous microscopical units called **cells.** Progress was slow and it was well over one hundred years before it was realised that growth was dependent upon the behaviour of these cells. A single cell was seen to give rise to two new cells apparently by dividing in half. It was not long before it was realised that growth depended upon such **cell division.** Thus cells could multiply and the pattern in which they subsequently became arranged determined the appearance of the mature organism. It was generally agreed that cells could arise only by the divisions of pre-existing cells and, moreover, that every plant and animal started its life as a single cell. But it was some years before the full implications of these facts were appreciated.

With the aid of even more powerful microscopes greater attention was paid to the contents of cells. In 1831 Robert Brown discovered that every cell contained a spherical body which he called the **nucleus.** Eleven years later Carl Nägeli noticed that at certain stages in the life of a cell the nucleus became transformed into a number of smaller bodies which were later given the name **chromosomes** by W. Waldeyer. And it was Waldeyer who pointed out that the transformation of nucleus into chromosomes must be highly significant since it always accompanied the reproduction, or division, of a cell.

Towards the end of the nineteenth century biologists began to realise that growth of the tissues of an individual was correlated with cell behaviour and that the division of a cell was always accompanied by regular changes of the nucleus. Soon it was found that the cell and its contents were involved, not only in the growth of an individual, but also in the process of sexual reproduction. In 1875 Oscar Hertwig showed that in animals the fusion of the nuclei of two special cells—the **sperm** from the male and the **egg** from the female—gave rise to a new individual. This was the process of **fertilisation.** Two years later Eduard Strasburger saw fertilisation in plants. This was a process basically similar to that observed by Hertwig in animals but the cells involved were the pollen grains and embryo-sacs. At last it was realised that the nucleus was the carrier of the hereditary material and that a new individual arising from sexual reproduction must contain hereditary material from both parents.

Gradually the information, which had been collected by various independent observers through the years, led to a clearer conception of heredity. August Weismann was one of the first to correlate the behaviour of cells and their contents with what was known of heredity at that time and it was he who postulated a mechanism whereby the inherited material could be passed on from one generation to another by means of the chromosomes.

While these important advances in the study of cells, or **cytology** as it is now called, were being made numerous experiments were being conducted in the breeding of plants and of animals, some of which have helped to establish our modern ideas of heredity. The experiments carried out by Gregor Mendel demonstrated the precise way in which characters were passed on from parents to offspring. In addition they showed that with a knowledge of the characters peculiar to an individual it was possible to predict with a great degree of accuracy how these characters would be inherited.

Mendel's contemporaries did not fully appreciate the importance of his conclusions which were soon forgotten. In 1900, however, three independent workers, De Vries, Correns and Tschermak, published the results of their experiments which were basically similar to those published by Mendel thirty-five years earlier. This was discovered when they started reading through earlier papers relevant to their own. Thus, **Mendel's Laws of Heredity** were widely accepted and became the foundation of the new science of **genetics.** Within three years it had been shown by Sutton that there was a striking parallel between the behaviour of chromosomes in the formation of germ cells and the Mendelian Laws of Heredity. At last the true relationship between heredity, growth and reproduction was established.

The extent of our knowledge to-day can be very briefly summarised as follows. We know that it is the hereditary material passed on from parent to offspring and contained in every living cell which determines the appearance of an organism and how it shall respond to its environment. This hereditary material is carried by bodies known as chromosomes which constitute the nuclei of the cells. These chromosomes are thread-like structures composed mainly of nucleic acids and proteins. The functional units of heredity are called **genes.** They are arranged in a linear order along the chromosomes and although they are too small to be seen the presence of each gene is confirmed by its own specific activity. For instance, in plants there are genes for such things as height, colour of flowers and shape of leaves, to mention but a few. A combination of the activities of all the genes determines the appearance, structure and behaviour of an individual. All the cells of an individual contain identical complements of chromosomes and therefore of genes. It is upon the behaviour of the chromosomes that the genes depend for their transmission from parent to offspring. Thus, when we are examining the structure and behaviour of chromosomes in the growth of an individual and in the formation of its reproductive cells we are, in a sense, looking at heredity.

2

MITOSIS AND DEVELOPMENT

FLOWERING plants which reproduce by sexual means develop from a single cell, called a **zygote,** which is the product of fertilisation. The development of this cell into a mature individual starts with its division, or to be more precise its reproduction, into two new cells. Each of the two cells then divides to give four, the four divide to give eight, and so on. (Fig. 1.) The process is repeated many times. But these divisions may not continue to occur synchronously and only a few cells may be dividing at any one time.

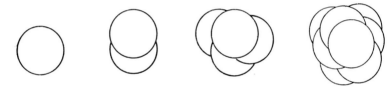

FIG. 1. Cell multiplication. Showing, diagrammatically, how eight cells may be derived from one cell. In this way a zygote develops into a young embryo.

The cells continue to multiply in this way until there are many millions of them and ultimately the young plant begins to take shape. Since all its cells arose from one cell, the zygote, they obviously have something in common. This is a most significant fact and one which is important, not only for the normal life of the plant, but also for that of its descendants in subsequent generations. The parts of the cell which are concerned with heredity are present in each and every cell in exactly the same form and amount with the exception, as we shall see later on, of those cells concerned in sexual reproduction. In other words, each cell has the same hereditary potentialities and therefore must have the same complement of chromosomes and genes.

The continuity of the hereditary material is ensured by a process called **mitosis** (Fig. 3) in which the division or reproduction of a cell takes place in a very precise and orderly manner. In plants there are tissues, such as the growing points of stems and roots, which are centres of active cell multiplication. (Plate I.) In these it is possible to examine mitoses in great detail and because of this we are now familiar with the main visible changes which occur.

Cells which are not actually in the process of division are usually said to be either in the **resting stage** or in **interphase.** The first term implies inactivity but this is far from being true. The second term is perhaps better since it merely suggests a stage between cell divisions. Each cell has its own wall. In plants this is composed mainly of cellulose and is usually a fairly rigid structure, although its shape can be influenced to some extent by the cells of the surrounding tissues.

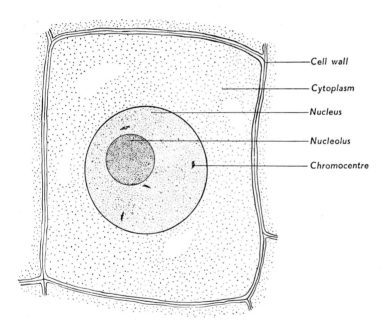

Fig. 2. Simplified diagram of a typical interphase cell from actively growing plant tissue.

The cell contains a viscous fluid with a system of membranes and numerous granular and rod-like inclusions. This is the **cytoplasm.** Within the cytoplasm lies the spherical **nucleus** with its own thin membrane. The interphase cell with its wall, cytoplasm and nucleus can be regarded as a working unit. Both the cytoplasm and nucleus are making and exchanging chemical substances. Some of these substances are used by the cell for its own reproduction, and some, after passing through the cell wall to associate with the products of other cells, are transported and used by the plant as a whole. Although the cytoplasm, as well as the nucleus, is involved in growth and heredity we must now focus our attention on the nucleus for here occur the visible changes associated with mitotic division.

During interphase the nucleus is composed of a number of **chromosomes** which are not individually distinguishable because they take the form of greatly extended threads. This gives the nucleus the appearance of a diffuse network. In some tissues which can be removed and cultured artificially and in which living cells can be examined, the presence of chromosome threads in the interphase nucleus has been confirmed. In some plants there are small regions of the chromosomes which remain visible even during interphase. These are known as **chromocentres** (Plate II and Fig. 2).

Every nucleus contains one or more spherical bodies called **nucleoli.** There is ample evidence that these nucleoli are formed close to small regions of some of the chromosomes called **nucleolar organisers.** The results of chemical analysis suggest that each nucleolus contains a mixture of various chemical substances including fats, proteins and nucleic acid. These may be used by the cell during the different phases of its development.

When an interphase cell has reached a certain stage of development, mitosis begins. The exact nature of the stimulus involved is, as yet, unknown. All we know is that a regular synthesis of nucleic acids, proteins and other substances must take place beforehand.

Mitosis begins with a stage called **prophase.** (Plates III and IV and Fig. 3.) The chromosomes which constitute the nucleus become visible as long threads each of which is divided along its length into two identical halves called **chromatids.** The chromatids of each chromosome are often twisted around each other. We know that the chromosomes are single threads at the beginning of interphase yet when they become distinguishable at prophase each is seen to have reproduced. This reproduction must have occurred during interphase or at the very beginning of prophase. Each chromosome has become transformed into two chromatids in such an exact way that these chromatids are completely identical. There is one small region of each chromosome, called the **centromere,** which is seen to be undivided at this stage. As we shall see it is not

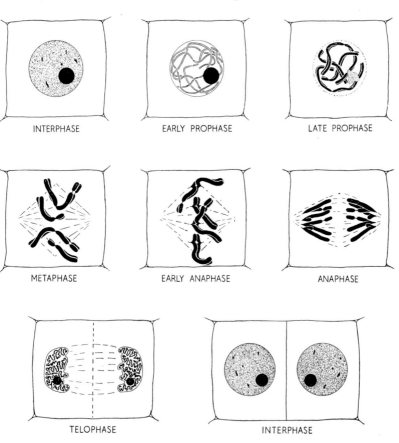

FIG. 3. Illustrating the main stages of cell division by mitosis in plants.

until much later that each centromere is seen to divide and play its highly specialised role.

As prophase proceeds the chromosomes gradually become more distinct due to a complicated system of coiling which leads to their contraction and thickening. (Plates V and VI.) While this contraction continues the nucleolus gradually disperses and it has been suggested that its contents may become transferred to the chromosomes. About the time that the chromosomes reach maximum contraction, the nuclear membrane breaks down and the contents of the nucleus mingle with the cytoplasm. This is the end of prophase.

The next stage, **metaphase,** is heralded by several changes in both the cytoplasm and the chromosomes. Once the nuclear membrane has broken down a new structure begins to develop in the cytoplasm. It seems to consist of a large number of delicate fibres which are orientated roughly parallel to one another and because of its general shape it is known as the **spindle.** The extreme ends of the spindle are called the **poles** and the central region, the **equator.** The optical properties of the spindle strongly suggest that it is composed of protein molecules longitudinally arranged to give a definite structure or pattern. Now the chromosomes move very gradually through the cytoplasm and become arranged on the equator in a special way. The centromere region of each chromosome comes into contact with the spindle. The centromere is still the only undivided portion and is marked by a constriction. These centromeres are always arranged in one plane across the equator but the free arms of the chromosomes are not necessarily restricted to any one position. By this time the chromosomes have attained their maximum degree of contraction. Metaphase has now been reached. (Plate VII and Fig. 3.)

Metaphase is the most favourable stage for the examination of individual chromosomes. As we have already seen each cell is a derivative of the zygote. The zygote is in turn derived from the fusion of nuclei from the parental germ cells. It is not surprising to find, therefore, that at the metaphase of mitosis there are two sets of chromosomes: one from each of the parents. In other words each chromosome has a *morphologically identical* partner. The number of chromosomes in each of the parental sets is known as the **haploid** number and together in the zygote, and hence in all the cells of the plant, they constitute the **diploid** number. However, it should be realised that, owing to their different origins, the chromosomes of each pair *will probably not be genetically identical* although, on morphological grounds, they are usually said to be homologous pairs.

The detailed examination of chromosomes at metaphase is facilitated by the use of certain drugs, the most effective of these being a complex organic compound known as colchicine which is obtained from *Colchicum autumnale*—the Autumn Crocus. Such drugs inhibit the formation of the spindle so that the chromosomes lie scattered freely in the cytoplasm instead of forming a compact group in one region of the cell. There is therefore less chance of chromosomes overlapping. At the same time the chromosomes become excessively contracted so that their various constrictions are more easily seen. (Plate VIII.)

Centromere

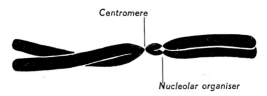

Nucleolar organiser

FIG. 4. One of the A chromosomes of *Lilium regale* showing the two types of constriction (*cf.* Plate VIII and Fig. 5).

Every chromosome has a centromere, sometimes known as the **primary constriction,** which occurs at a position which is constant for and characteristic of that particular chromosome. Some chromosomes have, in addition, a **secondary constriction.** (Fig. 4.) These constrictions mark the positions of the nucleolar organisers which we mentioned in our description of the interphase nucleus. It is at these sites that substances accumulate earlier in the mitotic cycle to form the spherical nucleoli. The constancy in position of both primary and secondary constrictions, together with the variation between chromosomes of the complement, provides a useful key to the identification of species and particularly of hybrids. (Fig. 5.)

The next stage in the mitotic cycle is **anaphase.** The centromeres, which at metaphase were the only undivided parts of the chromosomes, themselves divide so that each chromatid now has its own centromere. This change marks the very beginning of anaphase. The division of the centromeres appears to take place at the same time in all the chromosomes. The sister centromeres thus formed then appear to repel one another so that they move apart. This movement seems to be governed by the shape of the spindle and thus results in the drawing apart of the sister chromatids. It should be realised that this is a progressive separation which starts at the centromere region and continues along the chromatid arms towards the ends. (Plates IX and X and Fig. 6.) Observations on

B

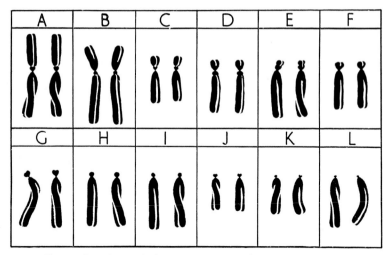

FIG. 5. Drawings of the 24 metaphase chromosomes of *Lilium regale* arranged as 12 homologous pairs with their centromeres, or primary constrictions, in line. Secondary constrictions present in A, B, C, D and E (*cf*. Plate VIII).

living cells have shown that anaphase movement is slow and it is therefore extremely difficult to follow by eye. But, by the use of time-lapse cinematography, accurate studies of the speed and mode of separation have been made. These studies have shown that the shape of the spindle and the viscosity of the cytoplasm are two of the many governing factors involved in chromosome movement.

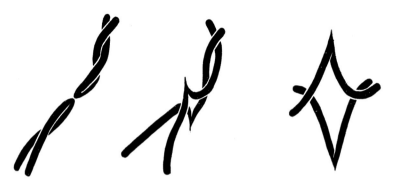

FIG. 6. Centromere division leading to the separation of the sister chromatids.

The sister chromatids, or chromosomes as they should now be called, continue their slow movement towards opposite poles of the spindle. (Plates XI, XII and XIII and Fig. 6.) At this later stage of anaphase the spindle itself undergoes certain changes. It lengthens and becomes narrower at the equator. This lengthening of the spindle is said to complete the anaphase separation of the daughter chromosomes which now form two closely-packed groups, one at each spindle pole. This marks the end of anaphase and the beginning of the next stage **telophase.** (Plates XIV and XV.)

During telophase the chromosomes behave in a manner which is, in many respects, the reverse of that seen during prophase. The chromosomes uncoil to become long thin threads and nucleoli begin to form. The chromocentres, so characteristic of many species of plants and animals, soon become evident. The chromosomes begin to form a typical interphase nucleus with the development of a nuclear membrane. These changes occur at exactly the same time in both daughter nuclei which, we must remember, are still within the same cytoplasm. Now, however, at the equator of the spindle a new cell wall begins to form which separates the two nuclei from one another and roughly divides the cytoplasm of the original cell in two.

Mitosis is complete and we have two new cells. (Plate XVI.) Looking back over the successive phases through which the chromosomes have passed we can fully appreciate the purpose and significance of the mechanism of mitosis. During mitosis every chromosome reproduces itself by dividing longitudinally and the reproduction of the chromosomes must, of course, be accompanied by the exact reproduction of the genes which they carry. When the daughter chromosomes separate at anaphase the genes are transported to opposite ends of the cell and it is here that the two daughter nuclei are formed. Thus the nucleus of each daughter cell will contain exactly the same genes as the nucleus of the original cell from which it was derived. In this way genetic continuity is ensured. These new cells may follow one of two main patterns of development. On the one hand they may pass through an interphase and undergo mitosis themselves to help build up a particular tissue. On the other hand they may not undergo a further mitosis before becoming modified in such a way as to fulfil a particular function.

When we consider that all the cells of a mature organism are derived from the zygote and are thus all genetically identical it is difficult to understand how various tissues and organs come to diverge so widely in both form and function. The formation of leaves, stems, roots, flowers and other organs is brought about by **differentiation,** a process about which much is still to be learned. We know that the properties of differentiation are inherited since they are expressed in the same way in each successive generation. It is also significant that isolated parts of plants in the form of root, stem and leaf 'cuttings' are capable of regenerating a new plant having characters identical with those of the plant from which they were originally taken.

As the nucleus is a body of such constant structure within cells of a wide variety of tissues we must look to other cell components for a possible explanation of the phenomenon of differentiation. Although the genes of the nucleus ultimately control the pattern of development they do so only in co-operation with the cytoplasm which is slightly variable since it is only roughly divided between daughter cells after mitosis.

It is generally assumed, therefore, that the way in which the nucleus acts—and this includes its ability to undergo mitosis—is dependent upon the cytoplasm. But it should be realised that the cytoplasm itself contains specific substances produced by the nucleus. It is this co-operation and interaction between nucleus and cytoplasm as well as that existing between neighbouring cells which brings about differentiation.

PLATES II TO XVI

MITOSIS IN ROOT-TIP CELLS OF *Lilium regale*

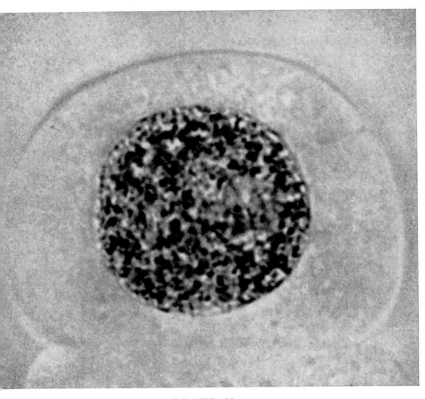

PLATE II

Interphase in a root-tip cell. The chromosomes are not individually distinguishable (× 2400).

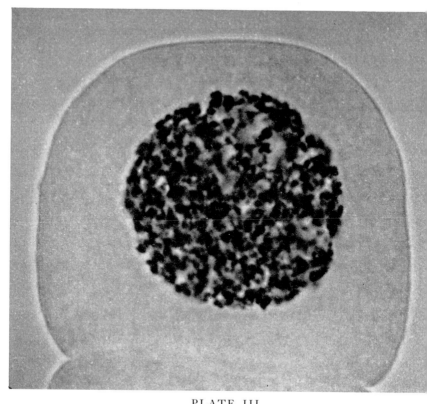

PLATE III

Prophase. The chromosome threads are just visible (× 2400).

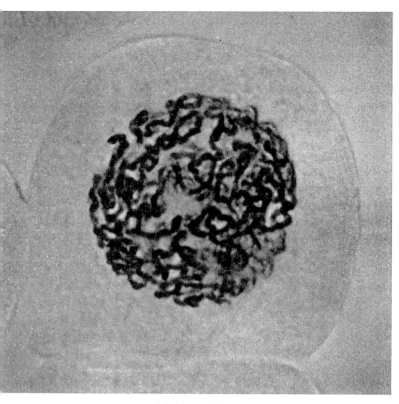

PLATE IV

Prophase. The chromosome threads are now quite distinct (× 2400).

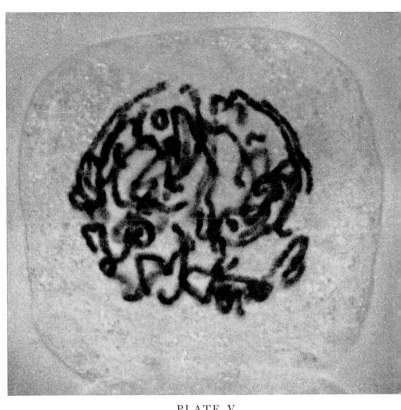

PLATE V

Prophase. The chromosome threads are shorter and thicker. Each is composed of two chromatids (× 2400).

18

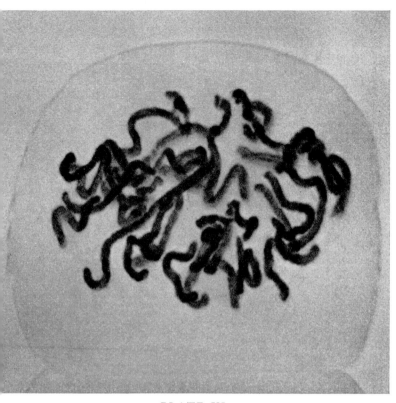

PLATE VI

Prophase. The chromosomes are reaching their maximum degree of
contraction and the nuclear membrane is breaking down (× 2400).

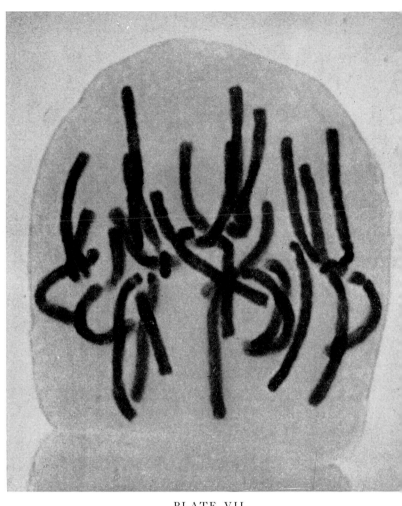

PLATE VII

Metaphase. The chromosomes have contracted further and they are now arranged upon the equator of the spindle. The spindle is not visible when the Feulgen staining method is used (× 2400).

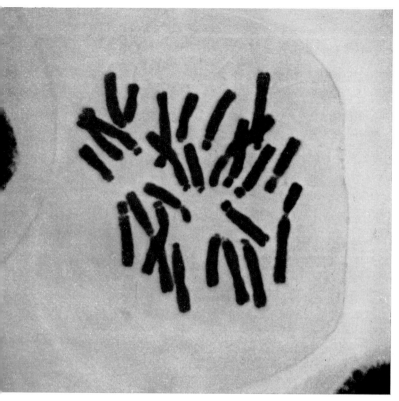

PLATE VIII

Metaphase. After colchicine treatment the 24 chromosomes and their centromeres, or primary constrictions, are clearly seen (× 2400).

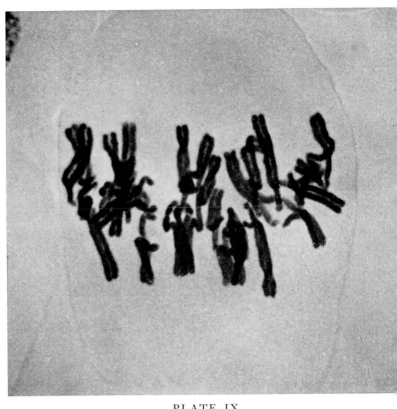

PLATE IX

Anaphase. The chromosomes are still arranged on the spindle equator but their centromeres have divided and are beginning to move apart (× 2400).

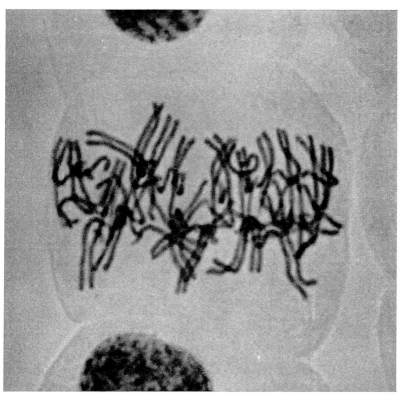

PLATE X

Anaphase. The centromere movement is continuing and the chromatids
are being separated (× 2400).

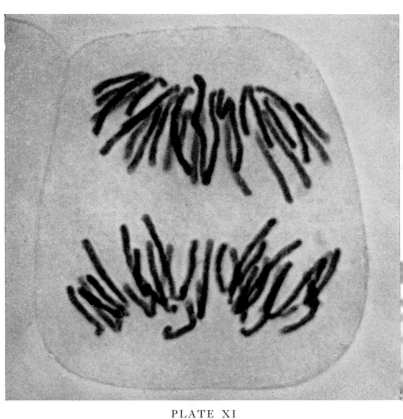

PLATE XI

Anaphase. The daughter chromosomes have separated and they are moving to opposite poles of the spindle (× 2400).

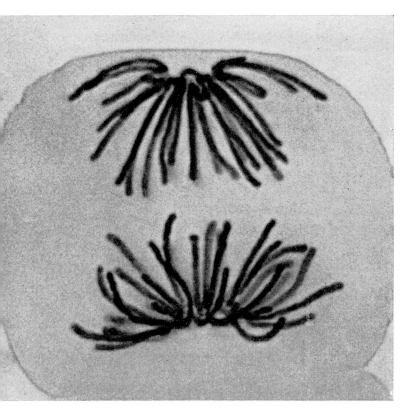

PLATE XII

Anaphase. The centromeres have reached the poles (× 2400).

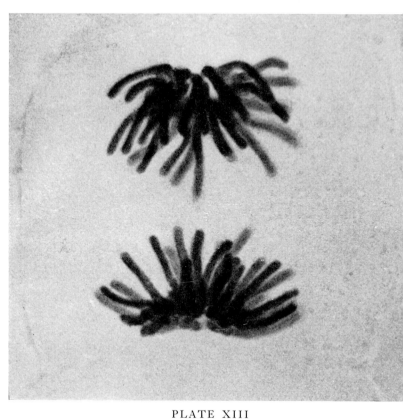

PLATE XIII

Anaphase. The daughter chromosomes are forming two distinct groups, one at each pole of the spindle (× 2400).

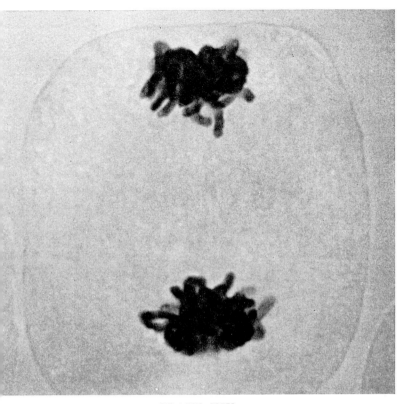

PLATE XIV

Telophase. The chromosomes are beginning to form the two daughter nuclei (× 2400).

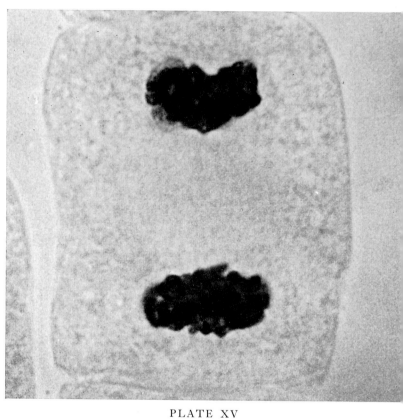

PLATE XV

Telophase. The chromosomes within the two daughter nuclei are no longer distinguishable. A cell wall is beginning to form between these two nuclei (× 2400).

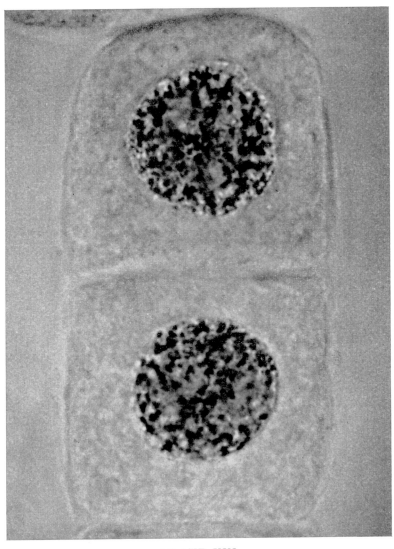

PLATE XVI

Interphase. Two new nuclei have now been formed which are completely
separated by the new cell wall (×2400).

3

MEIOSIS AND REPRODUCTION

As a plant develops towards maturity certain tissues become differentiated for the purpose of reproduction. This may be of the vegetative or asexual type where bulbs, corms, tubers and similar organs are produced. But in the majority of flowering plants sexual reproduction leading to the formation of seed is of more common occurrence.

Sexual reproduction involves the formation of specialised male and female germ cells within the **pollen grains** and **embryo-sacs** respectively. As we shall see, it is the fusion of special kinds of nuclei from these male and female cells, in a process known as **fertilisation,** which gives rise to a zygote: the first cell of the new individual. If the male and female nuclei each contained the same number of chromosomes as the other cells in the plant, that is the diploid number, an impossible situation would arise through fertilisation. In each successive generation the chromosome number would be doubled. Therefore a special process has evolved presumably by the gradual modification of mitosis, whereby this difficulty is overcome. This process is called **meiosis.** It comprises two divisions resulting in the formation of germ cells whose nuclei contain the haploid chromosome number. This is half the number found in the diploid cells of the rest of the plant. At the same time there is a re-assortment of the genes which has far-reaching consequences in heredity and evolution. (Fig. 7.)

(i) *The Formation of Pollen Grains*

The pollen is formed in the anthers of the young developing flower bud. In their early stages of development the anthers contain a mass of diploid cells undergoing numerous unsynchronised mitoses. These are at some later stage subject to a stimulus whose exact nature is as yet unknown. As a result their activities tend to become co-ordinated and progressively greater synchronisation of the mitoses results. (Plate XVII.) The degree of synchronisation in

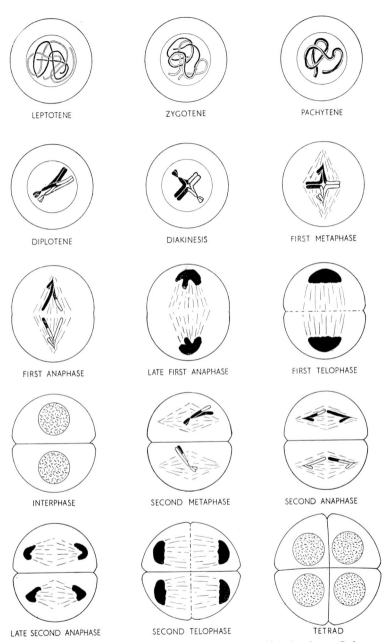

LEPTOTENE ZYGOTENE PACHYTENE

DIPLOTENE DIAKINESIS FIRST METAPHASE

FIRST ANAPHASE LATE FIRST ANAPHASE FIRST TELOPHASE

INTERPHASE SECOND METAPHASE SECOND ANAPHASE

LATE SECOND ANAPHASE SECOND TELOPHASE TETRAD

FIG. 7. Diagram illustrating the main stages of meiosis in plants. Only one maternal chromosome (white) and one paternal chromosome (black) represented for the sake of clarity.

these cells varies considerably between different species of plants but, when it has reached a certain stage and the **pollen mother cells** are formed, meiosis begins. This involves two nuclear divisions but only one division of the chromosomes.

Prophase is the first stage of meiosis. But as it is a longer and more elaborate stage than the prophase of mitosis it warrants further sub-division into the following stages—**leptotene, zygotene, pachytene, diplotene** and **diakinesis.**

Within the pollen mother cells at **leptotene** the nucleus is resolved into delicate, thread-like chromosomes which, because of their extreme length, are not individually distinguishable. (Plate XVIII.) At first sight leptotene resembles the prophase of mitosis but closer examination reveals important differences. First, the chromosomes are clearly *single* and not divided longitudinally into two chromatids as at mitosis. And, secondly, their structure is more definite. They somewhat resemble strings of beads due to the presence of dense granules, called **chromomeres,** which occur at irregular intervals along their length. Chromomeres are known to have characteristic sizes and positions on each chromosome and because of this they help in marking the positions of genes or groups of genes.

During leptotene, and throughout the entire prophase of meiosis, the chromosomes remain enclosed in a well-defined nuclear membrane. The nucleoli are very distinct during this period and are attached to the nucleolar organisers. The chromosomes are present in the diploid number as in the other cells of the plant. In other words, there is one set of chromosomes which originally came from the male parent and an homologous set from the female parent.

As the next stage, **zygotene,** is reached these homologous chromosomes begin to move. Each chromosome in one parental set has a partner of similar size and form in the other parental set. These pairs of chromosomes begin to come together by what appears to be a force of mutual attraction. This pairing of the homologous chromosomes begins at one or more points and gradually proceeds along their whole length in a 'zipper-like' fashion. (Plate XIX and Fig. 8.) It should be emphasised that pairing is a very exact process with chromomeres of similar size and at corresponding positions on each chromosome being brought together. While this is taking place the chromosomes are also undergoing a shortening and thickening which is typical of prophase whether it be in mitosis or meiosis. When pairing is accomplished it is so complete that the nucleus appears to contain the haploid number of chromosome threads. Only the most critical observation under the high-power microscope shows each thread to consist of a pair of homologous chromosomes. These pairs are known as **bivalents.**

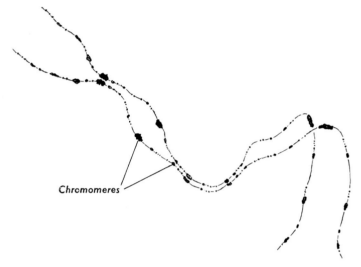

Chromomeres

FIG. 8. Part of a pair of homologous chromosomes at zygotene. Pairing between homologous regions has started (*cf.* Fig. 7).

During the next stage of prophase, **pachytene,** the chromosome threads become even shorter and thicker and in particularly favourable nuclei individual bivalents or parts of bivalents can be recognised by the characteristic arrangement of their chromomeres. (Fig. 9.) The centromere region and the point of attachment of the nucleolus can sometimes be seen and often act as further useful guides to the identification of bivalents.

The paired chromosomes of each bivalent become more intimately associated and, as pachytene proceeds, they often appear to become twisted around one another. As is to be expected the bivalents themselves will not associate with one another. (Plate XX.)

We have now summarised the visible changes of the chromosomes during pachytene, but there are other changes at this stage which are not visible but which have far-reaching genetical consequences. We infer that these changes have taken place in pachy-

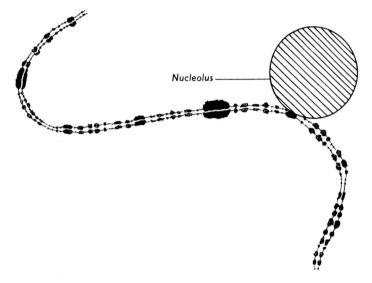

Nucleolus

FIG. 9. Part of a bivalent at pachytene showing complete pairing between the homologous chromosomes (*cf.* Fig. 7).

tene from the appearance of the chromosomes at the next stage of prophase which is known as **diplotene.**

A striking change in the appearance of the bivalents marks the beginning of diplotene. The mutual attraction between the pairs of homologous chromosomes now begins to lapse so that they are no longer in close contact along their entire length. There are, however, one or more places in each bivalent, called **chiasmata,** where contact is retained. (Plate XXI.) In particularly favourable cells it can now be seen that each chromosome is divided along its entire length except at one region, the centromere. The bivalent now consists of two pairs of chromatids. The chromosomes of each bivalent remain held together at the chiasmata because of a union which is formed at homologous regions. This is a special kind of union between chromatids in which only one chromatid of each chromosome is involved.

In contrast to zygotene and pachytene, where there appeared to be a force of mutual attraction between homologous chromosomes of each bivalent, we now see what appears to be repulsion. This results in the formation of loops between the consecutive chiasmata along the bivalent. Further contraction of the chromosomes takes place during this stage; the chromomeres become less distinct and the chromosomes themselves assume a rather 'woolly' appearance. But, before proceeding further with our description of meiosis, we should stop to consider the mechanism of **chiasma formation.**

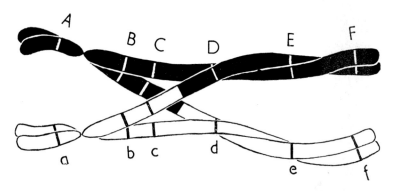

FIG. 10. A bivalent at diplotene with a single chiasma. Some of the genes are represented by letters. Crossing-over has occurred between one chromatid of the maternal chromosome (white) and one chromatid of the paternal chromosome (black).

Each chiasma provides visible evidence that there has been an exchange of parts of chromatids between the paternal and maternal chromosomes of each bivalent. The exchange itself is often referred to as **crossing-over** and the reason for this should become clear from Figure 10. Let us assume that the sequence of genes in part of *one chromatid* involved in the chiasma can be represented by

A B C D E F

and in the corresponding part of the *other chromatid* by

a b c d e f

Then, if a chiasma is formed in the chromatids between C and D and c and d, the genes in each chromatid will now become arranged as follows:

A B C d e f
and
a b c D E F

The actual mechanism whereby this exchange of chromatid parts, or crossing-over, is brought about must depend in some way upon the reproduction of each of the parental chromosomes forming the bivalent and the time at which it takes place. Unfortunately, the time of reproduction cannot, as yet, be fixed with any degree of certainty although it probably occurs long before the actual doubleness of the chromosomes is apparent under the microscope. Therefore, until more is known of the composition and behaviour of chromosomes during the early stages of meiosis, crossing-over is likely to remain a subject of great controversy. In spite of this, genetical experiments designed to investigate variation in the inheritance of characters have shown that genes can be re-assorted in this way by crossing-over.

Although the paired chromosomes in each bivalent are, in most cases, morphologically homologous it must be remembered that they originated from different parents and may well carry different complements of genes. The extent of this difference will depend upon the ancestry of the individual and its degree of hybridity. Each parental chromosome carries its share of the total complement of genes and these genes are arranged, as we have already stated, in a definite linear sequence upon each chromosome. This arrangement is strictly maintained by mitosis during the development of the individual, and it is only during meiosis that there can be a reciprocal exchange of chromatid parts so that new combinations of genes can arise. The extent of such gene recombination will naturally depend upon the number of chiasmata in each bivalent and this in turn is dependent upon the length of the chromosome. The distance between successive chiasmata is quite large in relation to the length of the chromosome. Thus the number of chiasmata occurring in each bivalent is comparatively limited. All the genes on a chromosome form what is called a **linkage group.** However, chiasma formation results in the sub-division of this linkage group into smaller groups. (Fig. 10.)

Before we can discuss the genetical implications of meiosis any further, it is essential to see how the chromosomes, which have been modified by crossing-over, behave in the final stages of meiosis and how they come to be distributed among the pollen grains.

Diplotene passes gradually into the next stage, called **diakinesis,** during which the paired chromosomes of the bivalents reach maximum contraction. (Plate XXII.) As contraction proceeds it can be seen that the consecutive loops between chiasmata come to lie in planes at right angles to one another. This gives the appearance of links in a chain.

The positions now occupied by the chiasmata do not necessarily represent the original points at which crossing-over occurred. The coiling and contraction of the chromosomes together with the repulsion between them leads to movement of the chiasmata towards the ends. This movement or slipping of the chiasmata is known as **terminalisation.** (Fig. 11.)

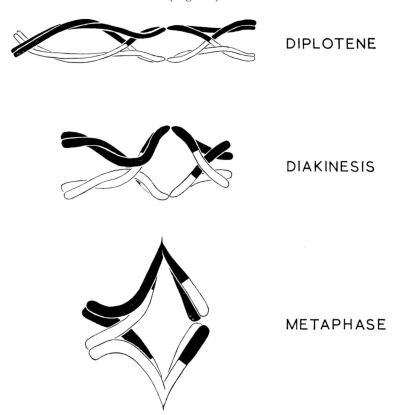

DIPLOTENE

DIAKINESIS

METAPHASE

Fig. 11. Showing the progressive changes in a bivalent, with two chiasmata, from diplotene to the first metaphase of meiosis. Contraction and thickening of the chromosomes accompany terminalisation of the chiasmata. At diakinesis and metaphase, therefore, the chiasmata no longer mark the positions at which crossing-over originally occurred.

The disappearance of the nucleolus and of the nuclear membrane marks the end of diakinesis, and therefore the end of meiotic prophase. A spindle is formed and the bivalents begin to move slowly through the cytoplasm towards the equator. As will be remembered, each bivalent consists of two chromosomes and thus each bivalent possesses two centromeres. These centromeres do *not* come to lie in one plane at the equator of the spindle. Instead the bivalents become orientated on the spindle so that their two centromeres lie one on each side of the equator and at equal distances from it. This is known as the **first metaphase of meiosis.** (Plate XXIII and Fig. 7.) The orientation does not necessarily result in all the centromeres of the maternal chromosome set lying on one side of the equator and all the centromeres of the paternal chromosome set lying on the other. The arrangement is completely at random.

The frequency and position of chiasmata, at first metaphase, vary between the pollen mother cells within an anther. For example, if one bivalent is particularly easy to distinguish from the others because of a striking difference in size, its appearance can be studied in different pollen mother cells. It can then be seen that the number and position of chiasmata vary from cell to cell and modify the shape of the bivalent accordingly. Some variation of chiasma frequency and position between pollen mother cells is quite characteristic of all species. It is by studying chiasmata that the cytologist is able to obtain valuable information about the parentage of a plant and to predict, to a certain extent, how fertile that plant is likely to be.

The next stage is the **first anaphase of meiosis.** The two centromeres of each bivalent which remain undivided begin to move away from each other towards the opposite poles of the spindle. At the same time the chromatids are gradually loosened and the chiasmata start slipping apart. (Plate XXIV.) The nature of the forces involved in the movement of centromeres has, so far, not been satisfactorily explained.

As the centromeres continue to move towards the poles they seem to pull their half-bivalents with them. (Plates XXV and XXVI.) But the rate at which the half-bivalents separate depends upon the length of the chromosome arms and the number of chiasmata which have to be drawn apart. The shape of the spindle begins to alter, as it does in a mitotic anaphase, and this accompanies the final separation of the half-bivalents to the poles. (Plate XXVII.) This is the **first telophase of meiosis** and now the chromosomes become uncoiled and form two nuclei which are usually separated by a cell wall which forms in the region of the spindle equator. (Plates XXVIII and XXIX.) The two cells are together known as a **dyad.**

It should be clear that after the first division of meiosis the chromosome number in each of the two nuclei is half that of the original nucleus of the pollen mother cell. Each now contains the haploid number. Moreover, these nuclei differ genetically for two reasons. First, as a result of crossing-over the combinations of genes on each chromosome has been altered. Secondly, even if there were no crossing-over, the random orientation of the maternal and paternal centromeres would, at anaphase, in itself lead to genetical differences between the two daughter nuclei.

The two nuclei then pass into **interphase.** (Plate XXX and Fig. 7.) This varies considerably in duration in different species of plants. In some cases it is merely a transitory phase with the chromosomes remaining clearly visible throughout. In other cases the chromosomes may form a nucleus which resembles that seen at mitosis. It should be pointed out here, however, that there are important differences. In mitosis the daughter chromosomes which go to form the interphase nucleus are single threads. On the other hand, the half-bivalents which go to form the interphase nucleus at the end of the first division of meiosis are clearly double threads, having divided prior to diplotene, and they are still held together by their undivided centromeres. There is no further reproduction of the chromosomes during the interphase of meiosis.

Interphase is a prelude to the last part of meiosis known as the **second division.** This division serves to separate the genetically different chromatids of each chromosome. At the end of the first division a cell wall is usually laid down between the two nuclei of the dyad. When such a cell wall is formed it is unlikely that the two nuclei will enter second division simultaneously. Where there has been no distinct interphase and the individual chromosomes have remained visible, the first telophase of meiosis passes imperceptibly into the **prophase** of the second division. In those organisms where the chromosomes uncoil at first telophase and become indistinguishable within the meiotic interphase nucleus the prophase of second division starts with the re-appearance of these chromosomes. (Plate XXXI.) In either case, as prophase proceeds, the chromosomes contract, thicken, become more distinct and can then be seen to be pairs of threads which are held together by a still undivided centromere. They have, in other words, remained structurally unaltered since the end of the first division.

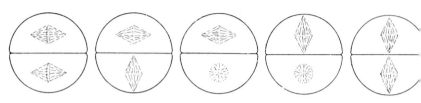

Fig. 12. Dyads at the second anaphase of meiosis showing some of the possible ways in which the two spindles can be orientated relative to one another.

At the end of prophase a spindle appears in each cell of the dyad. The orientation of the two spindles relative to one another varies within and between different groups of plants. (Fig. 12.) As in mitosis the chromosomes become arranged on the equator of the spindle. (Plate XXXII.) This is **second metaphase.** The centromeres divide at the beginning of **second anaphase** and the daughter chromosomes move to the poles. (Plates XXXIII and XXXIV.) At **second telophase** we then have four nuclei which eventually become separated from one another by new cell walls. (Plates XXXV and XXXVI.) Each cell is destined to become a pollen grain and the four cells are collectively known as a **tetrad.** (Plates XXXVII and XXXVIII.) Thus we have four potential pollen grains each with a haploid set of chromosomes and each differing from the others genetically, as shown in Figure 13.

Eventually, the four pollen grains separate, grow and begin to develop a thick wall which is often characteristically patterned. (Plates XXXIX and XL.) After a period of continuous growth the nucleus of each pollen grain undergoes a mitotic division. The time at which this **first pollen mitosis** takes place varies between different pollen grains within an anther. This lack of synchronisation is only to be expected when we consider that the nuclei of the pollen grains are genetically different. As a result two nuclei are formed, the **vegetative nucleus** and the **generative nucleus.** Although these nuclei are genetically identical they soon differ widely in appearance, the generative nucleus becoming compact while the

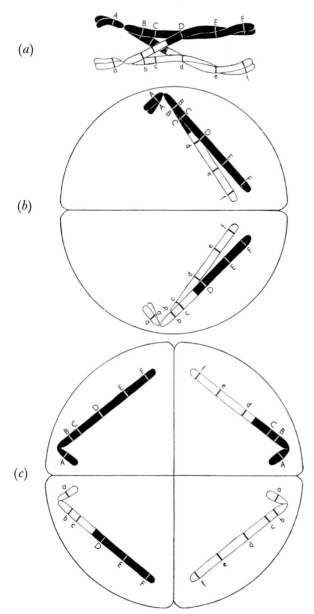

FIG. 13. The genetical consequences of crossing-over: (a) A bivalent at diplo-tene with a single chiasma. Some of the genes are represented by letters. Crossing-over has occurred between one chromatid of the maternal chromosome (white) and one chromatid of the paternal chromosome (black); (b) The half-bivalents in the dyad after the first division of meiosis; (c) The chromosomes in the four potential germ cells, each differing from the others genetically, after the second division of meiosis.

D

vegetative nucleus becomes diffuse and indistinct. (Fig. 14.) This is regarded as an example of differentiation *within* the cell, probably due to the activity of the cytoplasm.

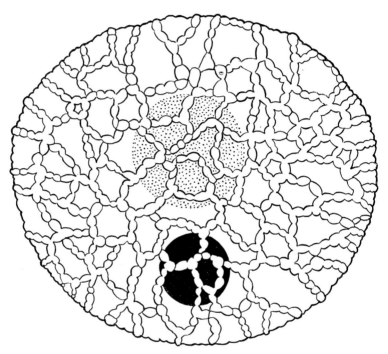

FIG. 14. Pollen grain of *Lilium regale* showing the characteristically patterned wall. The first pollen grain mitosis has resulted in the formation of a vegetative nucleus (stippled) and a generative nucleus (black).

While these changes are occurring within the pollen grains the growth of the flower bud continues until eventually it opens to expose the stamens and carpels. Throughout meiosis and during the early stages of pollen development the contents of the anthers are somewhat fluid. Now, however, rapid drying occurs and eventually the anthers split longitudinally to expose the pollen grains which may then be dispersed by movements of the air or by visiting insects. The pollen may come into contact with a stigma, which is the receptive region of the female reproductive organ and here it is stimulated to germinate. Each germinating pollen grain produces a tiny tube which is capable of growing down through the tissues of the style. (Fig. 15.)

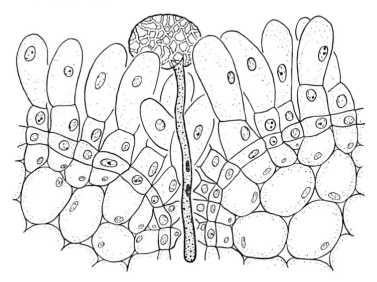

Fig. 15. Germination of the pollen grain on the surface of the stigma and the growth of the pollen tube down through the tissues of the style. The second pollen grain division has occurred and within the tube lie the two sperm nuclei.

The pollen grain is merely a carrier of the generative nucleus from which are derived two **sperm nuclei** which function in fertilisation. These two nuclei arise from the **second pollen mitosis.** The generative nucleus sometimes divides in the pollen grain and the two sperm nuclei then move into the pollen tube. In some species, however, the generative nucleus itself moves into the pollen tube before undergoing this mitosis. Of the many pollen tubes which grow down the style only one passes into an ovule. The two sperm nuclei pass to the end of the tube which then bursts so that they are discharged into the embryo-sac. Fertilisation now takes place but we will not discuss it until we have described the development and structure of the embryo-sac.

PLATES XVII TO XL

MEIOSIS AND THE DEVELOPMENT OF THE POLLEN IN *Lilium regale*

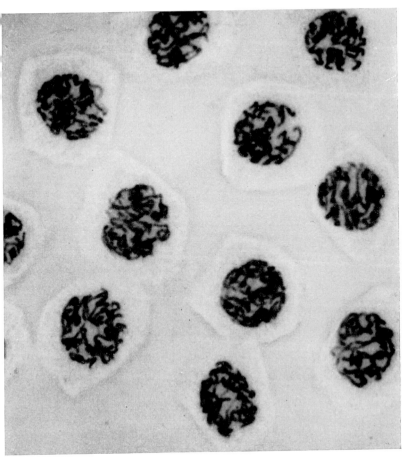

PLATE XVII

Nuclei synchronised at prophase of a pre-meiotic mitosis in a young anther (× 550).

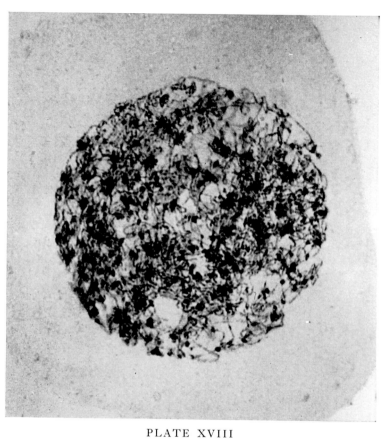

PLATE XVIII

Leptotene in a pollen mother cell. The nucleus is composed of 24 greatly extended chromosome threads (× 1700).

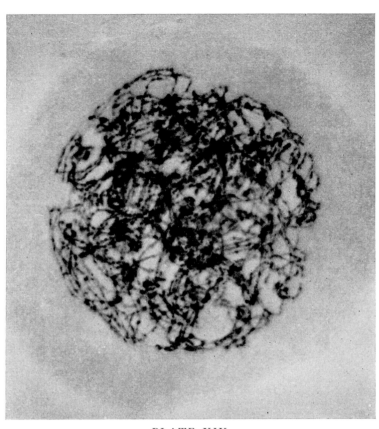

PLATE XIX

Zygotene. The chromosome threads have begun to associate in homologous pairs at various places along their length. Note the beaded appearance due to the presence of chromomeres (× 1700).

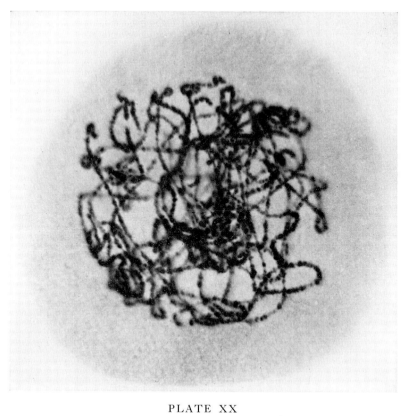

PLATE XX

Pachytene. Pairing of the homologous chromosomes is complete. The chromosomes have contracted and thickened and the chromomeres are now more obvious (× 1700).

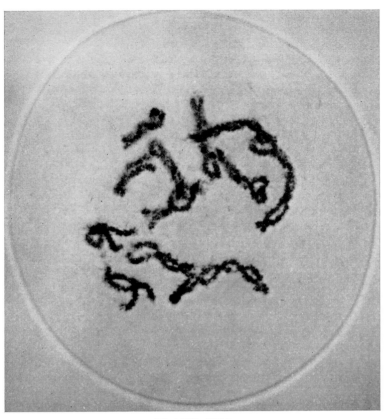

PLATE XXI

Diplotene. The chromosomes have contracted still further so that 12
bivalents are distinguishable. The attraction between the paired chromosomes of each bivalent has lapsed except where they are held together by
one or more chiasmata. Note the loops between consecutive chiasmata
(× 1700).

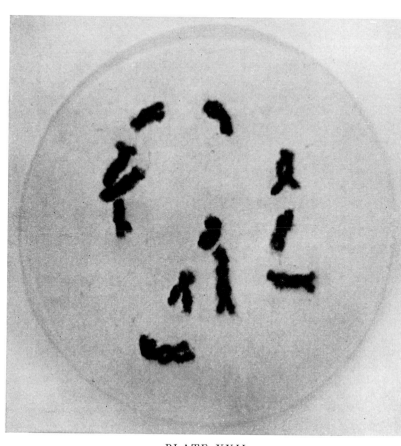

PLATE XXII
Diakinesis. The 12 bivalents have contracted further (× 1700).

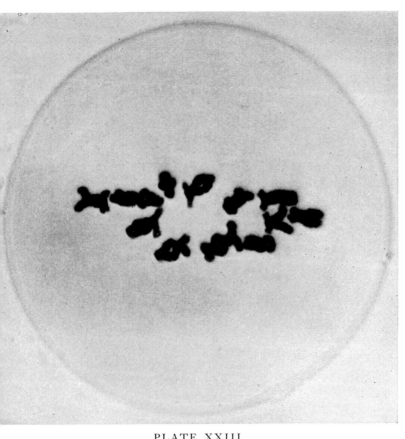

PLATE XXIII

First metaphase. The bivalents have become orientated upon the
equator of the spindle (× 1700).

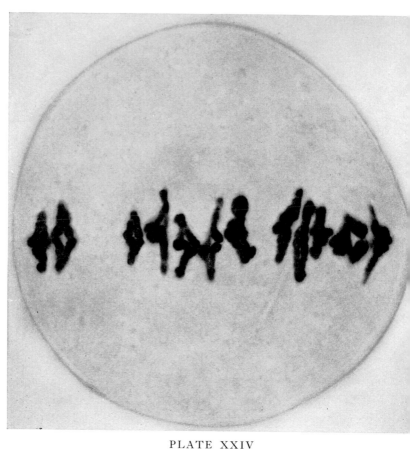

PLATE XXIV

First anaphase. Owing to centromere movement the half-bivalents are moving towards opposite poles of the spindle and the chiasmata are slipping apart (× 1700).

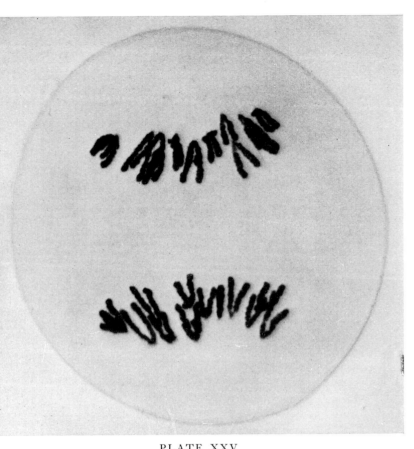

PLATE XXV

First anaphase. Separation is now complete and there are 12 chromosomes moving to each pole (× 1700).

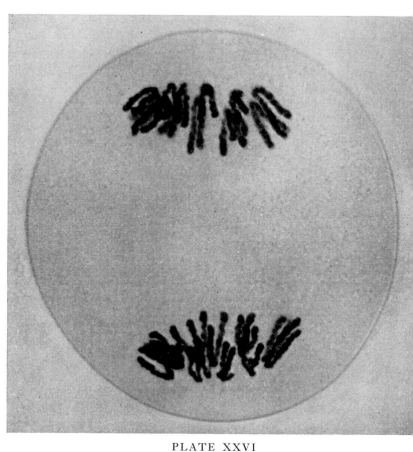

PLATE XXVI
First anaphase. The chromosomes have almost reached the poles
(× 1700).

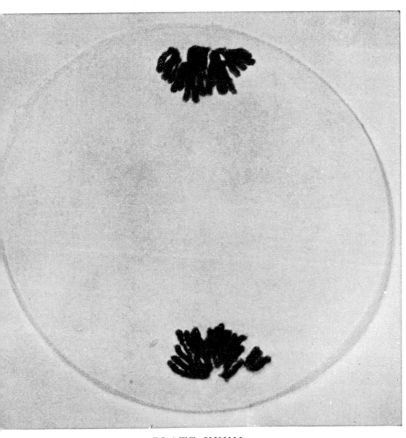

PLATE XXVII

First anaphase. The chromosomes having reached the poles now begin
to form two compact groups (× 1700).

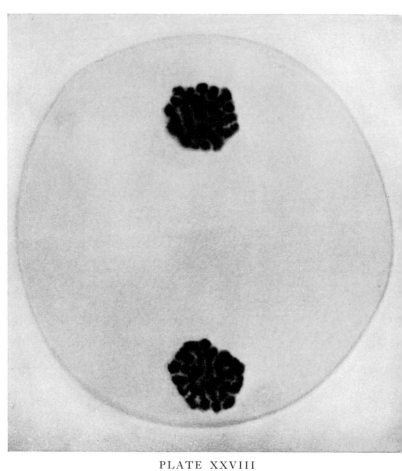

PLATE XXVIII
First telophase. The chromosomes have formed two nuclei (× 1700).

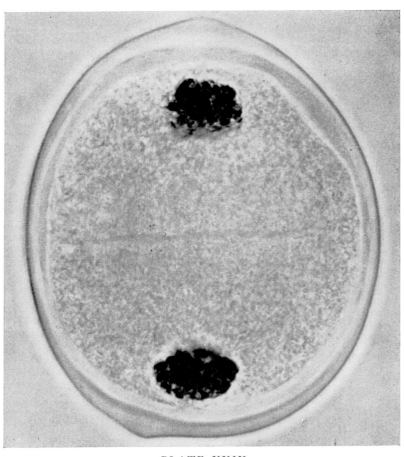

PLATE XXIX

First telophase. A new cell wall is beginning to form across the middle
of the cell to separate the two nuclei (× 1700).

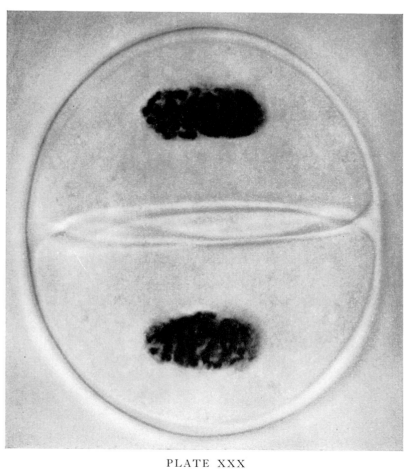

PLATE XXX

Interphase. Wall formation is complete and a dyad has been formed.
Each nucleus is composed of 12 chromosomes (× 1700).

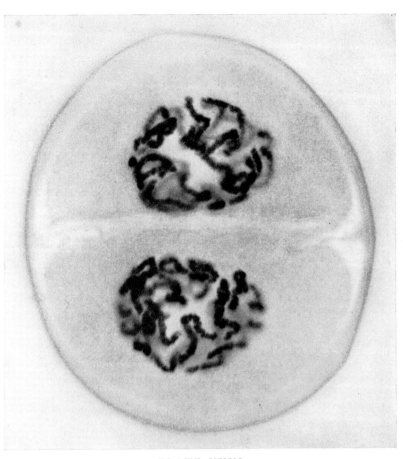

PLATE XXXI

Second prophase. The 12 chromosomes are now visible in each nucleus
(× 1700).

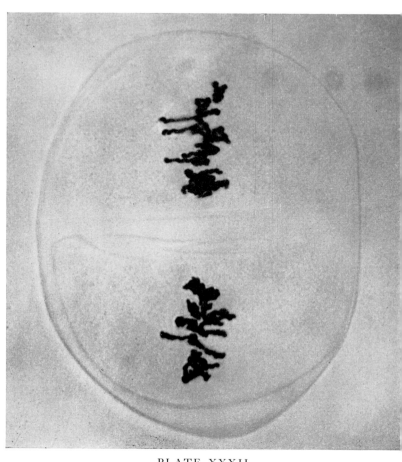

PLATE XXXII

Second metaphase. A spindle has formed in each cell of the dyad and the chromosomes have become arranged on the equators (× 1700).

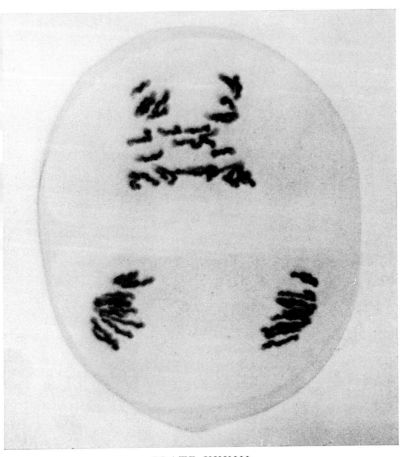

PLATE XXXIII

Second anaphase. The centromeres have divided and the chromatids
are separating. The two cells of the dyad are not synchronised (× 1700).

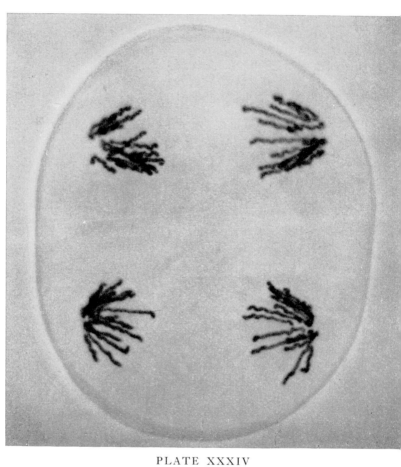

PLATE XXXIV

Second anaphase. An example of two synchronised cells of a dyad in
which anaphase movement is nearly complete (× 1700).

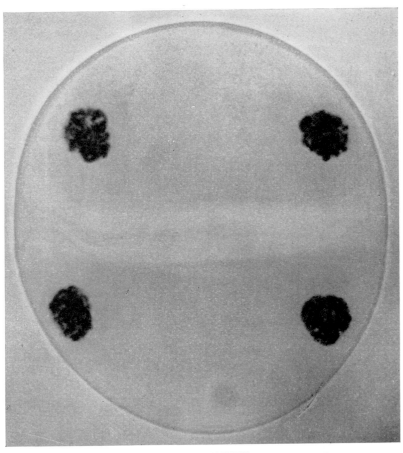

PLATE XXXV

Second telophase. The chromosomes have reached the poles and four nuclei have been formed (× 1700).

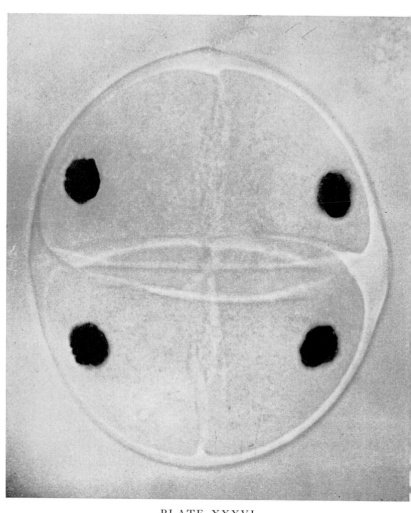

PLATE XXXVI
Second telophase. A new cell wall is developing (× 1700).

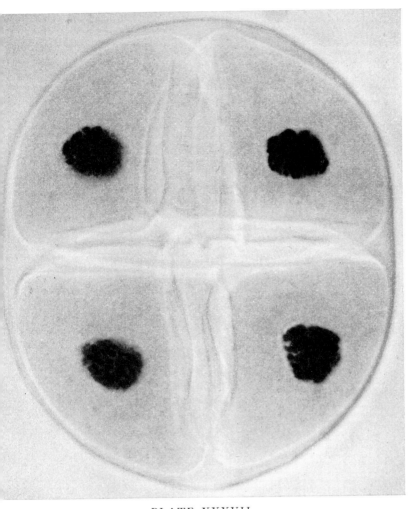

PLATE XXXVII

The tetrad. Four haploid cells have been formed. Each is a potential
pollen grain (× 1700).

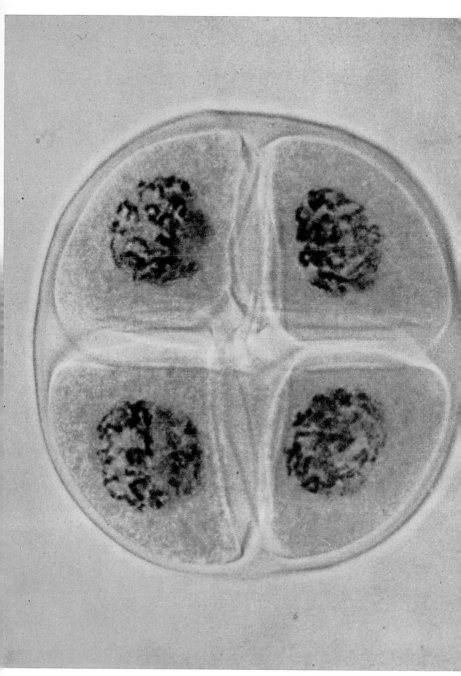

PLATE XXXVIII
The tetrad. The young pollen grains are developing (× 1700).

68

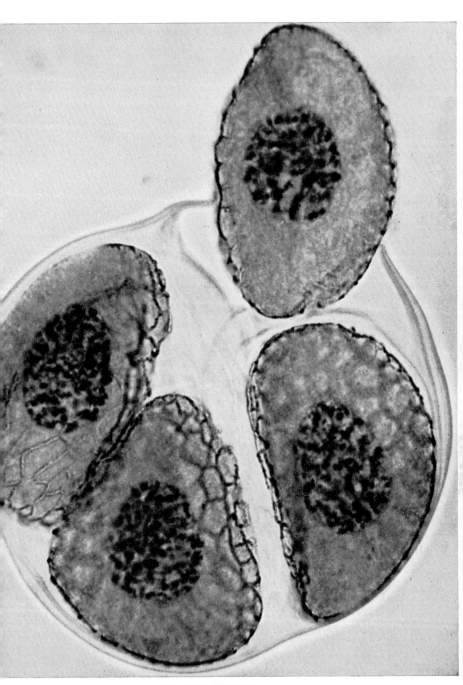

PLATE XXXIX

Young pollen grains. The four young pollen grains forming the tetrad are beginning to separate (× 1700).

69

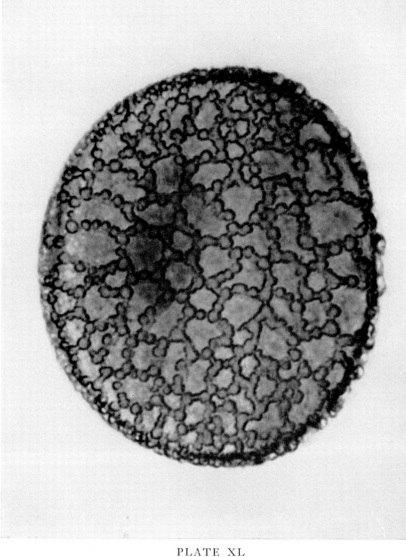

PLATE XL

Pollen grain. The wall has developed its characteristic patterning and the pollen grain is nearing maturity (× 850).

(ii) *The Formation of Embryo-Sacs*

We have already stated that during the growth of the plant certain tissues are differentiated for the purpose of sexual reproduction. The male cells, or pollen grains, are formed in large numbers within the anthers. The female cells, or embryo-sacs, occur singly and develop from one **embryo-sac mother cell** embedded in the tissues of a young ovule. This cell enlarges and frequently elongates so that it finally becomes much larger than a pollen mother cell at a similar stage in development. Meiosis in the embryo-sac mother cell is similar to that in the pollen mother cell and results in the formation of four haploid nuclei. (Plates XLI to XLVI.) This is the **primary four-nucleate stage** and it is comparable with the tetrad stage in the pollen mother cell. The way in which the embryo-sac continues its development varies considerably in different groups of plants. One, two, or even all four of the haploid nuclei may be concerned in the formation of a mature embryo-sac. Ultimately this can consist of from four to sixteen nuclei, the commonest number being eight. The final number of nuclei and their arrangement are determined by mitosis and by the migration of nuclei through the cytoplasm. In addition some of these nuclei fuse in a special way. For example, if two *haploid* nuclei undergo mitosis close together the chromosomes from both nuclei become orientated on one and the same spindle when the nuclear membranes finally break down. The daughter chromosomes, or chromatids, separate to form two nuclei each of which is then *diploid*. If, as sometimes happens, more than two nuclei are involved in a fusion the embryo-sac will contain not only haploid and diploid nuclei but also nuclei with higher multiples of the chromosome number. (Plates XLVII and XLVIII.) Only a few of these nuclei are functional in the process of fertilisation and the most important is the **egg nucleus** which, of course, is haploid. There are also two or more **polar nuclei** which function in fertilisation. They may be haploid, diploid or even polyploid according to the type of embryo-sac development. (Fig. 16.) The other nuclei, whose functions are unknown, are the **synergids** which often lie close to the egg nucleus and the **antipodals** which lie at the opposite end of the embryo-sac.

MEIOSIS AND THE DEVELOPMENT OF THE EMBRYO-SAC IN
Lilium regale

F

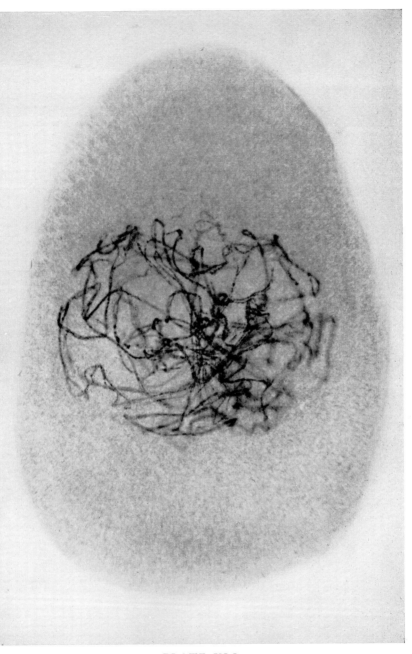

PLATE XLI

Zygotene in an embryo-sac mother cell (×8oo).

75

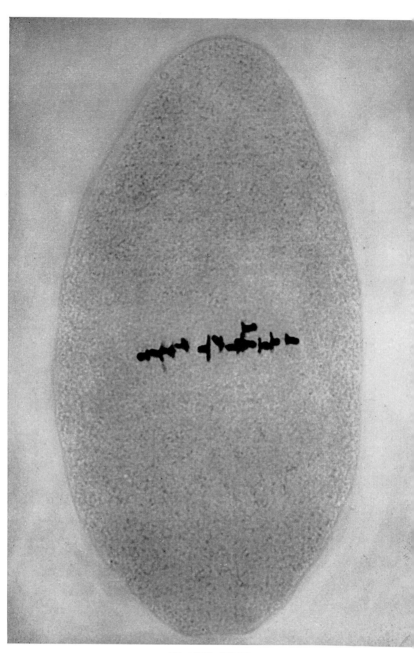

PLATE XLII
First metaphase (× 800).

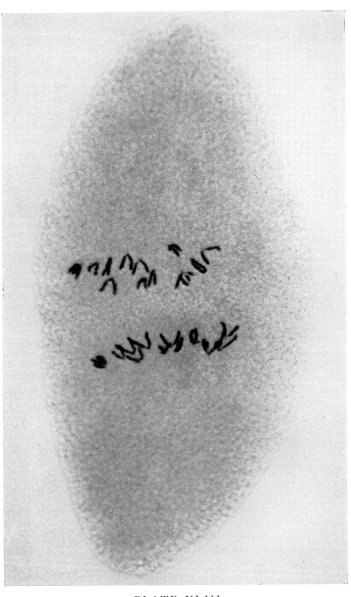

PLATE XLIII
First anaphase (× 800).

77

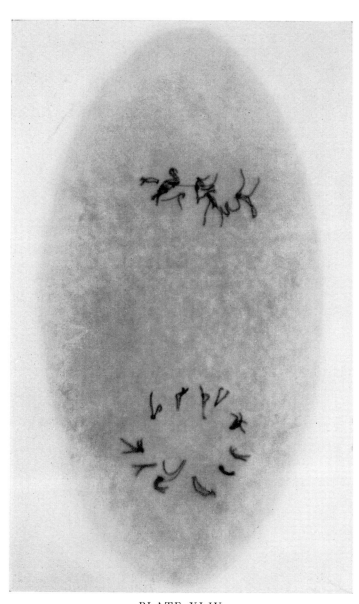

PLATE XLIV
Second metaphase (× 800).

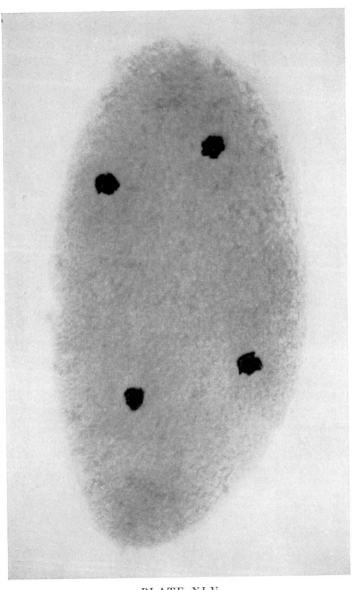

PLATE XLV
Second telophase (× 800).

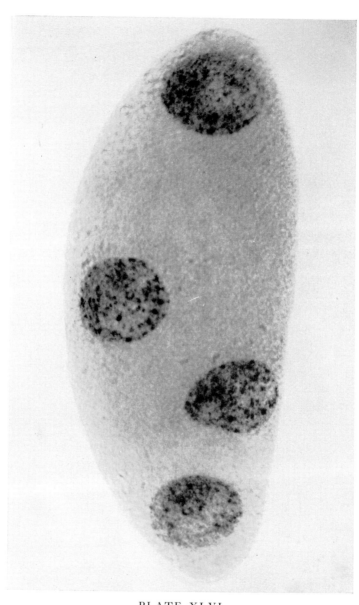

PLATE XLVI
Primary four-nucleate stage ($\times$ 800).

PLATE XLVII

Metaphases preceding the formation of the secondary four-nucleate stage. The chromosomes from three nuclei have come to lie on a single spindle at one end of the cell while at the other end there is a metaphase with the haploid number of chromosomes (× 800).

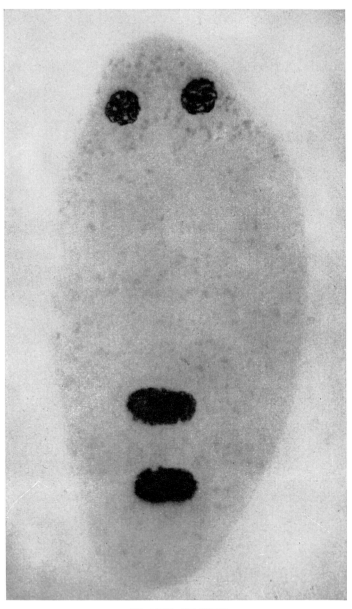

PLATE XLVIII

Secondary four-nucleate stage. One further mitosis of the two haploid and two triploid nuclei will give rise to a mature embryo-sac with four haploid and four triploid nuclei (see Fig. 16) (× 800).

82

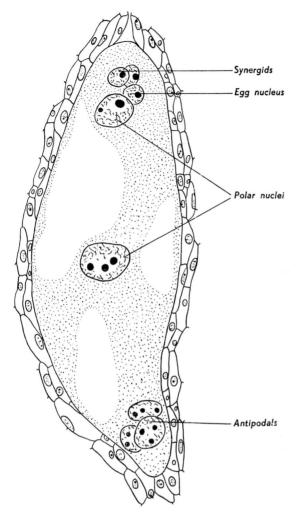

Synergids

Egg nucleus

Polar nuclei

Antipodals

FIG. 16. Diagram of a mature embryo-sac, of the type developed in *Lilium regale*, just before fertilisation.

(iii) *Fertilisation and the Formation of Seed*

As we have seen the pollen tube grows down the style and into the ovule where it bursts allowing the sperm nuclei to reach the embryo-sac. These sperm nuclei then pass through the cytoplasm. One comes into contact with the egg nucleus and the other with the polar nuclei.

There are conflicting reports concerning the behaviour of these closely-associated male and female nuclei. Some observations suggest that one sperm nucleus first becomes intimately associated with the egg nucleus and eventually unites with it to form the diploid nucleus of the zygote. Others suggest that the two nuclei remain closely associated without fusing until both nuclei enter mitosis. Then only one spindle is formed and the chromosomes from the male and the female nucleus become arranged on it to restore the diploid number. If fusion takes place at mitosis in this way we have not only the formation of the zygote but at the same time its primary division which results in the formation of the first two cells of the **embryo.**

Conflicting observations have also been made in connection with the union of the other sperm nucleus with the polar nuclei. The result of this union, however it may take place, is to form the **endosperm** which gradually increases in size by repeated divisions of its polyploid nuclei. (Fig. 17.) The function of the endosperm is to nourish the embryo in its early stages of development. This development is by no means haphazard because early differentiation of the cells ensures that the embryo shall grow in a regular way. The growing embryo with its nutritive endosperm and the surrounding tissues of the ovule form the young developing seed. In some plants the endosperm is absorbed by the embryo but in others, such as *Lilium*, the endosperm becomes multicellular and forms a large part of the mature seed when it is finally shed from the plant.

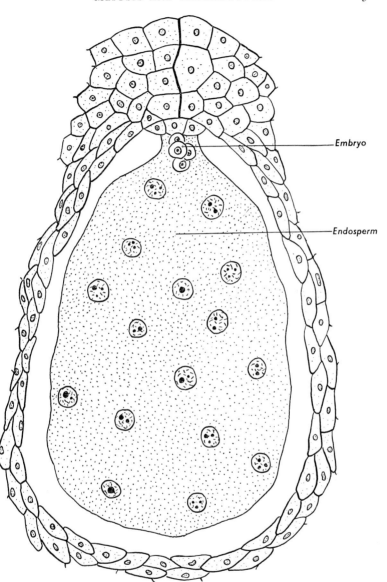

FIG. 17. An early stage in the development of the seed.

4

MITOSIS, MEIOSIS AND HEREDITY

W E have seen how a mature sexually-reproducing plant develops from the zygote, or fertilised egg cell, by mitosis and how meiosis occurs during the formation of the reproductive cells. (Fig. 18.) In describing these processes we

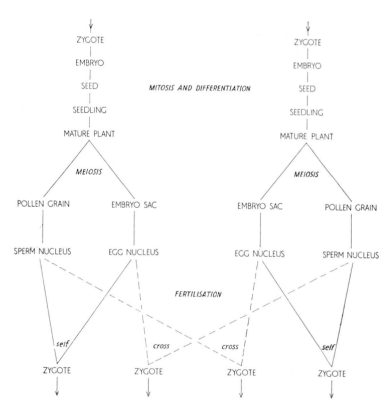

FIG. 18. Diagram illustrating some of the stages in the development and reproduction of two flowering plants and how new generations may arise through either self- or cross-fertilisation.

have concentrated mainly upon the mechanics of chromosome behaviour and we must now emphasise their far-reaching consequences in heredity.

At the time of fertilisation, when the chromosomes from the sperm and the egg nucleus together form the nucleus of the zygote, the genetic constitution of that zygote, and of the individual into which it will develop, is irrevocably established. The unerring precision of regular mitotic divisions ensures that this genetic constitution shall be maintained. The zygote develops into the embryo and the embryo into the young plant by mitotic divisions accompanied by differentiation. Although a variety of tissues and organs are differentiated the nuclei of the cells involved still contain identical complements of chromosomes and genes. These chromosomes and genes, inherited from the parents, will determine the character of an offspring and the way in which it will respond to its environment.

In plants which reproduce vegetatively, that is by means of bulbs, corms, rhizomes, stolons and so on, the chromosomes and genes are passed on entire and unchanged. Thus parents and offspring are identical both in appearance and in their response to the environment. A population of plants so formed is known as a **clone.** Although vegetatively-reproducing plants may be at an advantage in not having to rely upon favourable conditions for the production and germination of seed, their lack of genetic variability renders them static from an evolutionary point of view.

On the other hand, sexually reproducing plants are known to be capable of producing offspring which differ genetically from one another and from their parents. As we have seen, it is during meiosis that genes become re-assorted by crossing-over and finally distributed in new and varying combinations to the germ cells. In addition permanent changes, or **mutations,** can occur in genes so that their expression in the individual is altered. Such mutations occur spontaneously but comparatively rarely. They are also induced by radiation and certain chemicals. When one considers that the complement of genes in a parent is capable of being re-assorted in innumerable ways by crossing-over and modified by mutation one realises that there is enormous scope for variation. Later on, at fertilisation, it is the union of two germ cells which gives rise to a zygote and eventually a new individual with its own particular characteristics. New plants are continually arising, therefore, which have small genetic differences although they still retain the characteristic appearance of the species or taxonomic group to which they belong. Thus we have a mechanism whereby the variation of the plant population through consecutive generations provides for the adaptation of that population to new and changing environments.

5

APPENDIX

We recommend the following books for reference and further reading:

ABERCROMBIE, M., HICKMAN, C. J. and JOHNSON, M. L., *A Dictionary of Biology*. Revised ed. 1961. Penguin, London.

BONNER, D. M., *Heredity*. 1961. Prentice-Hall, New Jersey.

BURNHAM, C. R., *Discussions in Cytogenetics*. 1962. Burgess, Minneapolis.

DARLINGTON, C. D. and LA COUR, L. F., *The Handling of Chromosomes*. 3rd ed. 1960. George Allen and Unwin, London.

LEWIS, K. R. and JOHN, B., *Chromosome Marker*. 1963. J. and A. Churchill, London.

LEWIS, K. R. and JOHN, B., *The Matter of Mendelian Heredity*. 1964. J. and A. Churchill, London.

SRB, A. M. and OWEN, R. D., *General Genetics*. 1952. W. H. Freeman, San Francisco.

SWANSON, C. P., *The Cell*. 1960. Prentice-Hall, New Jersey.

WHITE, M. J. D., *The Chromosomes*. 5th ed. 1961. Methuen, London.

PRINTED IN GREAT BRITAIN BY ROBERT MACLEHOSE AND CO. LTD
THE UNIVERSITY PRESS, GLASGOW